GRADE BY GRADE

PIANO

GRADE 4

SELECTED BY
IAIN FARRINGTON

BOOSEY & HAWKES

Iain Farrington

Iain Farrington has an exceptionally busy and diverse career as a pianist, organist, composer and arranger. He studied at the Royal Academy of Music, London and at Cambridge University. He has made numerous recordings, and has broadcast on BBC Television, Classic FM and BBC Radio 3.

As a solo pianist, accompanist, chamber musician and organist, Iain has performed at all the major UK venues. Abroad he has given concerts in the USA, Japan, South Africa, Malaysia, China and all across Europe. He has worked with many of the country's leading musicians, including Bryn Terfel, Sir Paul McCartney and Lesley Garrett. Iain played the piano at the opening ceremony of the London 2012 Olympics with Rowan Atkinson, the London Symphony Orchestra and Sir Simon Rattle. He regularly performs with ensembles including the London Sinfonietta and the Britten Sinfonia, as well as all the major London orchestras.

As a composer, Iain has written orchestral, chamber, instrumental, vocal and choral works. He composed two orchestral works for the *Wallace and Gromit Prom* in 2012 including *Wing It*, a jazz guide to the orchestra. His organ suites *Fiesta* and *Animal Parade* have both been performed and recorded worldwide, and his choral work *The Burning Heavens* was nominated for a British Composer Award.

Iain is a prolific arranger in many styles, including traditional African songs, Berlin cabaret, folk, klezmer, jazz and pop. He is the Arranger in Residence for the Aurora Orchestra for whom he orchestrated all the songs in the *Horrible Histories Prom*. His organ arrangement of Elgar's *Pomp and Circumstance March No. 5* was performed at the Royal Wedding in 2011.

Published by Boosey & Hawkes Music Publishers Ltd
Aldwych House
71–91 Aldwych
London
WC2B 4HN

www.boosey.com

ISMN 979-0-060-12768-7
ISBN 978-0-85162-939-1

Second impression 2019

Printed by Halstan:
Halstan UK, 2-10 Plantation Road, Amersham, Bucks, HP6 6HJ. United Kingdom
Halstan DE, Weißliliengasse 4, 55116 Mainz. Germany

Music origination by Iain Farrington and Sarah Lofthouse
Piano performance by Iain Farrington
Aural Awareness recordings by Robin Bigwood
Cover design by RF Design (UK) Limited

CONTENTS

Arthur Benjamin	SOLDIERS IN THE DISTANCE from 'Fantasies for Piano'	2
William Byrd	LA VOLTA	4
Béla Bartók	TEASING SONG from 'For Children (volume 2)'	6
Carlos Gardel	POR UNA CABEZA	8
Peter Maxwell Davies	CALM WATER from 'Stevie's Ferry To Hoy'	12
Julius Fučík	ENTRANCE OF THE GLADIATORS	14
Henry Purcell	ROUND O	16
Serge Prokofieff	MARCHE from 'Musiques d'Enfants'	18
Christopher Norton	EARLY EVENING	20
Aram Khachaturian	SCHERZO from 'Pictures of Childhood'	22
Duke Ellington	RUDE INTERLUDE	25
Dmitri Kabalevsky	SONATINA from 'Thirty Pieces for Children'	26
Sergei Rachmaninoff	PIANO CONCERTO No 2 – first movement	30
Iain Farrington	STEPPING STONES	32
Dmitri Shostakovich	CLOCK-WORK DOLL from 'Six Children's Pieces'	34
Kenneth J Alford	COLONEL BOGEY MARCH	36
AURAL AWARENESS		11, 28
		(37, 38)
IMPROVISE!		10
SCALE SPOT	B♭ MAJOR	24
	C MINOR	29
	CHROMATIC	33
SIGHT-READING		9, 33

Note: All fingering has been added by composers or arrangers or taken from first published editions. Fingering has not been added to pieces where such markings do not feature in the original source material.

 FULL PERFORMANCE & AURAL AWARENESS CD

The enclosed CD contains demonstration tracks for all pieces plus audio for Aural Awareness tests. Track numbers are shown in grey circles.

SOLDIERS IN THE DISTANCE

from 'Fantasies for Piano'

Arthur Benjamin was an Australian musician who worked for much of his life in England as a composer and teacher. This work is taken from his 'Fantasies for Piano', published in 1933, and is a brilliant depiction of a far-off march. The soft pedal should be used throughout, while there is virtually no sustaining pedal, apart from where marked. Drums are imitated with the low left hand chords, and the music should always be kept as soft as possible.

ARTHUR BENJAMIN
(1893–1960)

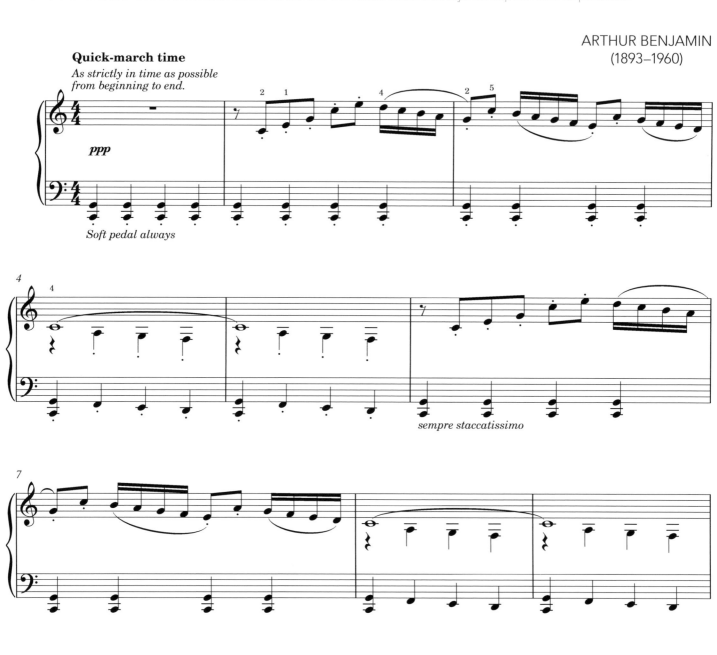

3

LA VOLTA

This piece is taken from the 'Fitzwilliam Virginal Book', a manuscript collection of nearly three hundred keyboard works by English composers that dates from around 1560–1610. William Byrd was one of the foremost Elizabethan English composers, especially in the realm of sacred music. 'La volta' was a dance of the period, and the piece should be played with rhythmic energy and lift.

WILLIAM BYRD
(c1539–1623)

TEASING SONG

No 18 from 'For Children (volume 2)'

Composed in 1908–9, 'For Children' is a collection of pieces based on Hungarian and Slovakian folk tunes.
'Teasing Song' is a lively, upbeat work, notable for its offbeat rhythms and the sudden tempo changes at the end.

BÉLA BARTÓK
(1881–1945)

POR UNA CABEZA

Carlos Gardel was a singer-songwriter born in France but raised in Argentina, and he was revered for his performances of the tango. Written in 1935, 'Por Una Cabeza' (meaning 'by a head') compares a horse race to the follies of love. The characteristic tango rhythm in the left hand should be precise, with plenty of attack from bar 19.

CARLOS GARDEL
(1890–1935)
arr IAIN FARRINGTON

SIGHT-READING 1

Look for the clues about how this piece will sound:

1. Is the piece major or minor? Name the key.
2. What does **Andantino grazioso** mean?
3. What does $\frac{6}{8}$ mean exactly? Clap the rhythm of the music in the left hand at bar 4.
4. Note all the dynamic markings. Describe the character of the last two bars.

Set yourself a steady pulse and off you go!

PAUL HUGHES

IMPROVISE!

In this exercise we'll use some of the features of Gardel's **Por Una Cabeza** (page 8) to create an improvisation in the style of a tango.

The left hand has a two-bar descending bass line which should be repeated throughout the piece. It uses a typical tango rhythm (known as a 'habanera'). Practise these two bars without using your right hand until they become second nature, and be sure to emphasise the phrasing and articulation.

In the right hand, four chords are notated (with matching chord symbols written above) and you are to improvise a melody using any notes from those chords. The chords change every minim, so the palette of notes available to improvise with changes pretty quickly!

You might like to start with a simple repeating rhythm in the right hand which you can play with notes from the chords. Here's an example, but you should use your own rhythm and choice of notes.

Now it's time to add more interest to your improvisation melody. Try to use a variety of different rhythms. You don't need to play notes constantly – rests are effective in defining phrases and adding contrast. Once you're really comfortable with the style and notes available you can even add in other notes that sound good. Don't worry about making 'mistakes' – go with the flow.

Here's an example of how your improvisation might begin:

AURAL AWARENESS 1

This activity will help you to better understand and enjoy the music that you hear and play. Like your fingers, your ears need a little practice, so try these activities with your teacher, listening to the CD, or to your teacher as they play the piano.

TASK A – MUSICAL FOUNDATIONS

Listen to this short piece and see how many of the questions you can answer. You will need to listen to it three or four times.

- Clap the pulse; is it in two, three or four time?
- Is the piece in a major or a minor key?
- How loud or quiet was the playing? Was it the same all the way through the piece?
- The tune moves between the two hands. Describe where this happens.
- Sing the first few bars of the tune.

TASK B – INTERVALS

18

You will hear three pairs of notes from the melody – a low note first, then a higher note. Each pair will be played twice. Describe the interval formed by each pair.

There should be two parts to your answer:
1. the type of interval (major, minor or perfect)
2. the distance (2nd, 3rd, 4th or 5th)

(It might help to sing all the notes of the scale from the low note to the higher one that is played, counting on your fingers. The lowest note will be '1'.)

TASK C – SPOT THE DIFFERENCE

You will hear the key-chord and tonic, then a short phrase from the same tune played twice. There will be one change in the second playing.

- Is the change in the rhythm or the pitch?
- Describe the change, singing or clapping if it's helpful to do so.

TASK D – CADENCES

A cadence in music is like punctuation in text, signifying a pause in or conclusion of a phrase. Listen to the first two cadences – you will hear the tonic and key-chord first, and then the cadences – each is formed of two chords played one after the other.
The first is a 'perfect' cadence, and the second is an 'imperfect' cadence.

20

Here is another cadence (preceded by the tonic and key-chord). Is it 'perfect' or 'imperfect'?

21

A **perfect cadence** feels like the end of a phrase – it's a bit like a full stop.
An **imperfect cadence** sounds as if the music needs to continue – it's more like a comma.

Here are two more cadences to identify – are they perfect or imperfect?

CALM WATER

from 'Stevie's Ferry To Hoy'

Peter Maxwell Davies has enjoyed a prolific career in all musical genres, and was Master of The Queen's Music from 2004 to 2014. 'Stevie's Ferry To Hoy' was composed in 1976 and is inspired by a boat crossing in the composer's home of the Orkney Islands.

PETER MAXWELL DAVIES
(b 1934)

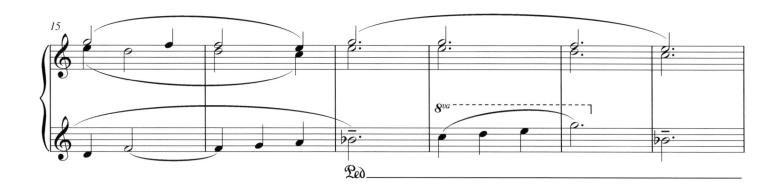

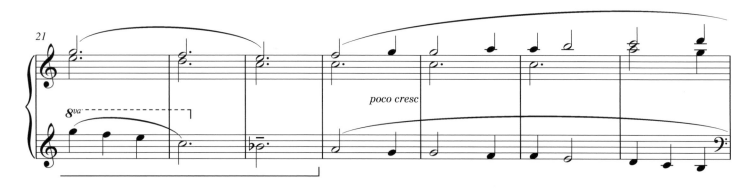

ENTRANCE OF THE GLADIATORS

Julius Fučík was a Czech composer and conductor, well-known for his work with military brass bands for whom he composed many marches. His most famous piece is 'Entrance of the Gladiators', also known as 'Thunder and Blazes', composed in 1899. Although intended to evoke Roman history, the work is now associated with the circus, in particular with clowns.

JULIUS FUČÍK
(1872–1916)
arr IAIN FARRINGTON

ROUND O

Henry Purcell was organist at Westminster Abbey where he wrote much sacred music, but he was also a prolific composer for the theatre. He composed incidental music for the play 'Abdelazar' in 1695, which includes this 'Rondeau'. Benjamin Britten used the theme for a set of variations in 'The Young Person's Guide to the Orchestra' of 1946.

HENRY PURCELL
(1659–1695)

MARCHE

from 'Musiques d'Enfants'

Prokofieff composed a number of works for children in the 1930s, partly for pleasure but also due to pressure from the Soviet authorities in Russia at the time. This piece is taken from 'Music for Children' (op 65) from 1935, later orchestrated by the composer as 'Summer Day'. A strict tempo is essential, with a dry touch.

SERGE PROKOFIEFF
(1891–1953)

EARLY EVENING

Play this cool jazz tune with a real lightness of touch. Ensure that you swing all the quavers.

CHRISTOPHER NORTON
(b 1953)

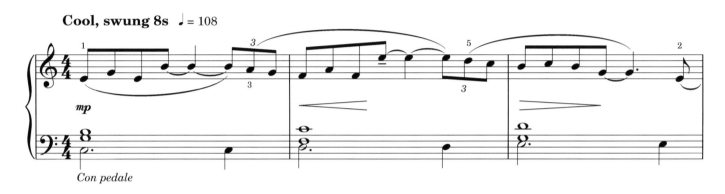

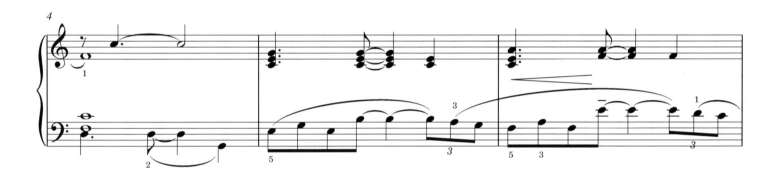

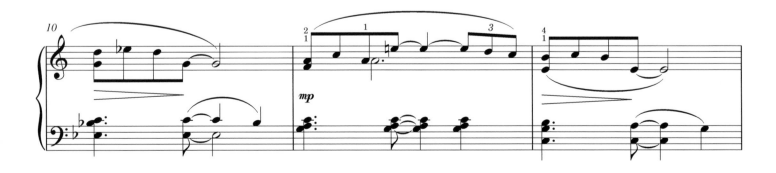

SCHERZO

from 'Pictures of Childhood'

10

Aram Khachaturian was an Armenian composer who gained great success with his orchestral music and ballets, especially 'Gayaneh' and 'Spartacus'. This piece is part of his 'Pictures of Childhood' composed in 1947 and requires a very even tone as the melody passes between the hands.

ARAM KHACHATURIAN
(1903–1978)

SCALE SPOT

Rude Interlude (opposite) is written in the key of **B♭ major**.
The B♭ major scale contains two flats – B♭ and E♭.

Practise playing the scale (below) – what fingering will you use to create a smooth and even sound?
Once you can play it *legato*, why not experiment using different phrasing and dynamics?

Here is a B♭ major scale exercise. Practise it hands separately and together.
When you're comfortable with the notes, try making the exercise your own by adding different dynamics and articulation.

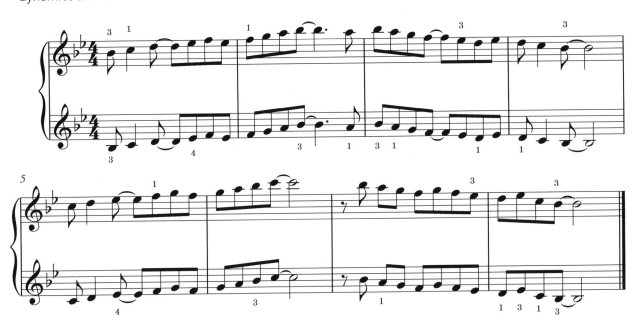

The exercise below is based on the B♭ major arpeggio to practise hands separately and together.
What fingering will you use to ensure this sounds as smooth as possible?

RUDE INTERLUDE

Duke Ellington was a pianist, bandleader and composer whose work was pivotal to the development of jazz. 'Rude Interlude' was composed and recorded in 1933 by his band, and has a steady bluesy feel. Whilst the right hand is smooth, the offbeat chords in the left hand should be dry and sound very rude!

DUKE ELLINGTON
(1899–1974)
arr IAIN FARRINGTON

SONATINA

from 'Thirty Pieces for Children'

Kabalevsky was an important figure in music education in 20th century Russia, and composed a large amount of children's music. This is from his 'Thirty Pieces for Children' from 1937-8. The short notes in the dotted rhythms need to be quick and precise so as not to sound like lazy triplets.

DMITRI KABALEVSKY
(1904–1987)

AURAL AWARENESS 2

This activity will help you to better understand and enjoy the music that you hear and play.
Like your fingers, your ears need a little practice, so try these activities with your teacher,
listening to the CD, or to your teacher as they play the piano.

TASK A – MUSICAL FOUNDATIONS

Listen to this short piece and see how many of the questions you can answer.
You will need to listen to it three or four times.

- Clap the pulse; is it in two, three or four time?
- Is the piece in a major or a minor key?
- How loud or quiet was the playing? Was it the same all the way through the piece?
- Describe the character of the music.
- Sing the first few bars of the tune.

TASK B – INTERVALS

You will hear three pairs of notes from the melody – a low note first, then a higher note. Each
pair will be played twice. Describe the interval formed by each pair.

There should be two parts to your answer:
1. the type of interval (major, minor or perfect)
2. the distance (2nd, 3rd, 4th or 5th)

(It might help to sing all the notes of the scale from the low note to the higher one
that is played, counting on your fingers. The lowest note will be '1'.)

TASK C – SPOT THE DIFFERENCE

You will hear the key-chord and tonic, then a short phrase from the same tune played twice.
There will be one change in the second playing.

- Is the change in the rhythm or the pitch?
- Describe the change, singing or clapping if it's helpful to do so.

TASK D – CADENCES

A cadence in music is like punctuation in text, signifying a pause in or conclusion of a phrase.
Listen to the first two cadences – you will hear the tonic and key-chord first, and then the
cadences – each is formed of two chords played one after the other.
The first is a 'perfect' cadence, and the second is an 'imperfect' cadence.

Here is another cadence (preceded by the tonic and key-chord). Is it 'perfect' or 'imperfect'?

A **perfect cadence** feels like the end of a phrase – it's a bit like a full stop.
An **imperfect cadence** sounds as if the music needs to continue – it's more like a comma.

Here are two more cadences to identify – are they perfect or imperfect?

SCALE SPOT

The movement from Rachmaninoff's second piano concerto overleaf is in the key of **C minor**.

Using a pencil add accidentals to make this the scale of **C harmonic minor**:

Add accidentals here to make this the scale of **C melodic minor**:

Here is the **C harmonic minor contrary motion** scale.
What fingering will you use to make this sound as smooth as possible?

This is an exercise based on the C harmonic minor contrary motion scale.

PIANO CONCERTO No 2 – first movement

One of the composer's most popular works, this concerto was composed as a way out of depression and creative block that had afflicted Rachmaninoff for several years. It is dedicated to Nikolai Dahl who had given him hypnotherapy to restore his self-confidence, and the work was premiered in 1901. The surging main theme is passionate and brooding, and a free use of pedal is encouraged.

SERGEI RACHMANINOFF
(1873–1943)
arr IAIN FARRINGTON

STEPPING STONES

14

This piece is taken from 'Night Journey', a set of 24 miniatures of varying character composed in 2004. The musical material is made up of the 'perfect fifth' interval, which hops around from place to place. It should be dry and give the effect of a string orchestra plucking the strings (*pizzicato*).

IAIN FARRINGTON
(b 1977)

SCALE SPOT

Unlike a major or minor scale, a **chromatic scale** is made up solely of semitone steps. Practise playing chromatic scales starting on any black note – hands separately at first, and then hands together.

SIGHT-READING 2

Look for the clues about how this piece will sound:

1. What key is this piece in? Which two bars contain all the notes of its scale?
2. What is a **Waltz** and what are its key musical features?
3. Note all the dynamic markings and phrasing.

Set yourself a steady pulse and off you go!

PAUL HUGHES

CLOCK-WORK DOLL

from 'Six Children's Pieces'

Amongst his vast output as a composer, Shostakovich composed educational pieces, including those included in 'Six Children's Pieces'. 'Clock-work Doll' is the sixth piece in the set and requires precise rhythm as well as nimble fingers.

DMITRI SHOSTAKOVICH
(1906–1975)

COLONEL BOGEY MARCH

'Colonel Bogey March' was composed in 1914 by Lieutenant F J Ricketts, a bandmaster in the British Army who wrote under the pseudonym Kenneth Alford. It became a national favourite and was notably used in the 1957 film 'The Bridge on the River Kwai'.

KENNETH J ALFORD
(1881–1945)
arr IAIN FARRINGTON

AURAL AWARENESS 1 (page 11) ⑰ ⑱ ⑲ ⑳ ㉑ ㉒

TASK A – MUSICAL FOUNDATIONS

Play the piece once and ask your student to clap in time with your piano playing as soon as they are able, emphasising the strong beats. Ask whether the piece is in two, three or four time. (This piece is in three time.)

Now play the piece again, repeating as necessary, and ask your student whether the piece is in a major or minor key (major), how loudly or quietly the piece was played, and whether the dynamics were the same all the way through. (The piece started quietly (*piano*). There was a *crescendo* and the music became louder (*forte*), before becoming suddenly quieter again (*piano*). The second half of the piece was louder.)

Ask your student to describe where the tune moves between the two hands, before inviting them to sing the first few bars of the tune. (The melody moves from the right hand to the left hand halfway through the piece, before returning to the right hand at the end.)

PETER TCHAIKOVSKY

extract from 'Tchaikovsky Album for the Young – 21. Sweet Dreams'

TASK B – INTERVALS

Play each of the three pairs of notes below twice. Ask your student to describe each interval.
Answers: 1. perfect 5th, 2. perfect 4th, 3. minor 2nd.

(continued)

TASK C – SPOT THE DIFFERENCE

Play the tonic and key-chord (C major) and tonic, then count in and play the two phrases below. Ask your student whether there is an alteration in the pitch or the rhythm of the second phrase and to describe the change using singing/clapping as necessary. (There was a pitch change at the beginning of the extract; the third note was lower.)

TASK D – CADENCES

Sound the tonic and key-chord (C major) before playing the first two cadences below, and discuss how the first forms a perfect cadence and the second an imperfect cadence. Play the tonic and key chord, before asking your student to identify the third cadence (C major) (imperfect), and then the final two cadences (Eb major, A major) (perfect, imperfect).

AURAL AWARENESS 2 (page 28) ㉓ ㉔ ㉕ ㉖ ㉗ ㉘

TASK A – MUSICAL FOUNDATIONS

Play the piece once and ask your student to clap in time with your piano playing as soon as they are able, emphasising the strong beats. Ask whether the piece is in two, three or four time. Answer: This piece is in two time.

Now play the piece again, repeating as necessary, and ask your student whether the piece is in a major or minor key (minor), how loudly or quietly the piece was played, and whether the dynamics were the same all the way through. (The piece started quietly (*piano*) and became louder (*mezzo forte*) halfway through.

Invite your student to describe the music's character, before asking them to sing the first few bars of the tune.

DMITRI KABALEVSKY

TASK B – INTERVALS

Play each of the three pairs of notes below twice. Ask your student to describe each interval.
Answers: 1. perfect 5th, 2. major 2nd, 3. major 2nd.

TASK C – SPOT THE DIFFERENCE

Play the tonic and key-chord (D minor), then count in and play the two phrases below. Ask your student whether there is an alteration in the pitch or the rhythm of the second phrase and to describe the change using singing/clapping as necessary. (There was a rhythmic change at the end of the extract; the penultimate note was shorter.)

TASK D – CADENCES

Sound the key-chord (D minor) and tonic before playing the first two cadences below, and discuss how the first forms a perfect cadence and the second an imperfect cadence. Play the tonic and key-chord, before asking your student to identify the third cadence (D minor) (perfect), and then the final two cadences (E major, C major) (perfect, imperfect).

NOTES